Looking for Jonathan

*How a Simple Focusing Exercise
Saved a Child From the Nightmare
of A.D.D.*

T. Whitney Strickland, Jr.

Xulon Press
11350 Random Hills Road
Suite 800
Fairfax, VA 22030
(703) 279-6511
XulonPress.com

To order additional copies,
call 1-866-909-BOOK (2665).

Contents

Forword
by Dr. Michael F. Zoda

Attention Deficit/Hyperactivity Disorder (ADD) is a true medical condition. It may be over-diagnosed, however it is a real problem for those who indeed have the disorder. While much is being learned in the area of brain physiology there is also much more that remains to be understood.

A child with ADD has problems with inattention and/or hyperactivity/impulsivity. The disorder manifests in a variety of ways. The inattention component is characterized by a lack of attention to details (e.g. careless mistakes), problems with sustaining attention in activities (but not all activities), not listening when spoken to, lack of follow through with instructions, difficulty organizing life tasks, reluctance to do work that requires sustained concentration (e.g. homework), often losing important items (e.g. toys, books, school assignments), being easily distracted, and being often forgetful. The hyperactivity component is characterized by fidgeting with hands or feet, moving around when not allowed (e.g. leaving seat in classroom), difficulty "playing quietly," incessant motion, excessive talking. The impulsivity is characterized by interruptions into others' conversations, blurting out answers before being asked, or difficulty waiting for one's turn.

To be classified clinically as ADD, six or more of the symptoms must be present to a degree that causes significant problems for the child. Some of the symptoms must be present before age seven and the symptoms must be present in at least two settings (e.g. school and home).

Clinicians are being taught a bio-psycho-social model for mental health. This model acknowledges the complexity of interacting systems from which human behavior emerges. ADD has a biological component tied into brain physiology. It also has a powerful impact on the developing personality of a child with ADD. Finally, a child who is ADD dramatically impacts the relationships both within a family and in the larger social contexts of school, church, and peers.

It is out of my background as a family therapist for the past thirteen years that I have interacted with Mr. Strickland in his pursuit of his son. Mr. Strickland most assuredly also deals with ADD. However, two aspects of this disorder (as well as his true faith in Jesus Christ) were instrumental in his development of the protocol, which is the basis of this book. Because of the varied ways a person with ADD learns, they often are very creative thinkers. Ironically, individuals with ADD often also possess an inordinate ability to doggedly pursue an area of interest. Mr.

Strickland is both highly creative and powerfully motivated toward a topic on which he is currently focused. His ability to "think outside the box" was the critical element, which took the general principles of the ADD diagnosis and the behavioral parenting applications, which I relayed, to him to a new place. It is his intense love for his son and his tenacious motivation to "find Jonathan" each morning that has provided the consistency a parent must have for this protocol to be of long term use for an ADD child.

This protocol has no research basis at this point. I must admit I have been skeptical for much of its development. However, after talking to Mr. Strickland, Jonathan, and Jonathan's first and second grade teachers, I believe something quite unexpected has occurred in Jonathan's ability to relate in school and at home. He is much more focused, attentive, and self-assured. Jonathan's ability to process information, make good choices, and follow instructions is at a level far beyond the developmental maturation I would have expected in the ten months over which this protocol has been used by him and his father.

I hope this protocol will be researched extensively. At this point it is imperative that parents know their children well enough to determine if the child needs this protocol and whether its implementation is helpful. If there are any questions about these issues, a mental health professional should be consulted.

Ultimately, I hope this protocol will be helpful to a large number of children and their families. If such is the case, to God be the glory.

Dr. Zoda is a Marriage and Family Life Therapist in Tallahassee, Florida.

Looking for Jonathan

The path to saving Jonathan was painfully personal and littered with a range of emotions which only a frightened parent of an Attention Deficit Disorder child can fully understand. Initial denial, then fear and hopelessness gave way to an intense drive, born of pain and bathed in tears, to do whatever was necessary to help our son. Through prayer and pursuit, God delivered a mental exercise now given to my child each morning. It doesn't take long, about twenty-five minutes, but it means the difference in saving my child from another day in the hell that is ADD. The result is that Jonathan is no longer a waiting failure but rather a model student leading his second grade class. Equally important is the extraordinary social and judgmental maturity he has gained over the last ten months. Whereas he used to be socially removed and had difficulty in making friends independent of his older brother, he now comes home excited about his day, talking about his best friend Cody and uttering those words that every ADD parent longs so desperately to hear—"I had a GREAT day at school." I have been warned that the experts and people with a vested interest in keeping our children on drugs would brand this story as just another half baked idea. So be it. For personal reasons, I have to write these words and I have little to gain or lose by sharing them. If a parent is encouraged by our experience and another child positively affected, that will be enough for me.

The family afflicted by ADD becomes accustomed to nightmares and to being wounded daily. The parents are stressed, other non-ADD children feel denied, and the attention deficit child is often lost spiraling down the path of low self esteem and depression. ADD lurks, wounds everyone around and then hides like a coward and a thief. But nothing wounded our family as deeply as watching our handsome, bright son reach for the sky only to fail time after time. There are no words for the pain. And the pain was made more intense by a deep belief that if we could just get to Jonathan, with a little bit of help, he could be all that God made him to be. We knew he was wonderfully made. We just didn't know where he was. With this in mind, we went looking for Jonathan.

I will give thanks to Thee, for I am fearfully and wonderfully made; Wonderful are Thy works, And my soul know it very well.

Ps. 139:14.

Our search began in the fall of 2000 when Jonathan entered first grade. It now seems so long ago. It also seems strange that we had lived with Jonathan for so long but had no idea he was lost. In fact, we were full of optimism at the thought of watching Jonathan grow and mature in the school which had so perfectly nurtured our older son. After all, we had plenty of reason to expect immediate success. At various times during Jonathan's preschool years, he had taken simple IQ tests for which he was given a very high score. Although he had not been the most outstanding student in kindergarten, we attributed this to the fact that he had attended preschool in another system- one which was not as challenging as the new school. Even with this disadvantage, he had done relatively well and had improved greatly during the year. The kindergarten teacher had been very satisfied with his achievements.

So it was that we approached the new year full of hope and without concern over what the future might bring. Then came the first week's graded papers. Much to our surprise, the papers reflected grades all over the grading scale, some of which were graded F or unsatisfactory. My wife and I discussed this and, although we were taken aback, we agreed that it certainly must be the result of the first week jitters. We knew this bright little child would do much better during the following week. Wrong again. The next week more school papers arrived at our home with grades once again all over the grading scale. The impact these papers had on us as parents now seems a bit odd. Although the second week's papers were very much like the first week's, somehow we were again very much surprised. I suppose we simply expected immediate improvement and felt certain that by the second week, the problem would have resolved and we would be well into our much anticipated dream of success. We felt strongly this confidence was well founded. Jonathan had consistently demonstrated a remarkable knack for saying clever things and was most capable of coming up with surprisingly novel thoughts for a small child. Indeed the family would often remark that Jonathan could do things no one else could do. This explains our happy optimism. As the weeks went by, we continued to believe that we would see better school work. The next few weeks, however, brought similar papers to our home and with them a sinking feeling that something might be horribly wrong. But we had no idea what the problem might be and we still did not know Jonathan was lost.

Although puzzled by his school performance, we just knew Jonathan had the ability to be a successful student. Still we were at a loss at what to do. So I began to pay very close attention to the child's behavior. What I saw presented quite a curious picture. Although Jonathan was normally happy at home, he was often very frustrated in the morning before school. This could be seen in that before getting out of bed, Jonathan would often scream loudly and angrily while kicking his feet. When this happened, he would be very slow to rise and would be terribly obstinate and disobedient. Most often he would refuse to get dressed in the morning until he created a confrontation with a parent who would have to discipline him. Worse yet, the discipline did not seem to work. Too many times, after punishment, Jonathan would sit down by the door, woefully cry and continue to fight getting dressed by fitting and refitting his shoes and socks. This happened almost daily and made the entire family miserable, particularly me, as I began to focus on a problem that seemed to have no shape or form. The children were quite often arriving at school after the tardy bell.

It was clear that Jonathan was starting to hate school and was trying to avoid going by the only means he knew. What was unclear was why. What I know now and was about to discover is that Jonathan is ADD. A certain coldness awaits the ADD child every morning. It's a coldness born out by the reality that the new school day will bring more disappointment and failure and also the fear of disappointment and failure. The disappointment and failure will be public and it will be humiliating. It will come in the form of a teacher's disapproving glance, the laughter of his classmates or a failing grade received on a test covering material the child fully understands. Worse yet, no one will be there to help or to comfort the child. And the child will suffer alone and in silence because he has never known anything different than a day of disappointment. And the loneliness only grows because each failure is met with punishment and public and private condemnation. The ADD child can only absorb partial information because he or she can pay attention only part of the time. This means that the ADD child makes poor judgments socially and scholastically because the judgments are based on only partial information. Other children turn from the ADD child and this in turn increases the isolation and the coldness of the morning and it explains why Jonathan would cry out when it was time to go to school.

After school brought more problems. When his mother picked him up from school, Jonathan would cry and scream if his mother needed to do an errand which would delay going home. She finally stopped going anywhere but home to avoid the confrontation which would surely result from a short trip anywhere else. Once home, however, the problems continued. Jonathan would refuse to work with his mother on homework. If she attempted to work with him, he would fight her even to the extent of accidentally striking her. When she tried to explain things to him, he would complain and cry mournfully that she had not explained anything at all and that he did not understand. The temper tantrums so emotionally exhausted my wife that she finally told me she could not work with the child and that I would have to be responsible for Jonathan's homework.

In early September, we called Jonathan's teacher and set an appointment. Unreasonable as it may seem, we were still anticipating a pleasant meeting with the teacher who would tell us Jonathan was progressing well and that she was looking forward to a year of outstanding success. Wrong again. The teacher told us that although Jonathan was doing well in some subjects such as math, a subject with a clear and definite answer, he was having trouble in subjects requiring judgment and insight such as reading. He also seemed to do poorly in activities which require paying attention. The teacher then mentioned the possibility of a processing error. Now that got our attention. I knew enough about child development to realize that a processing problem could be a major mental health issue and a life long difficulty. She also told us Jonathan was having problems with interacting appropriately. She said he would not laugh or smile even when it was appropriate to do so such as when a joke was told or a funny story was being read. This sounded so odd because at home Jonathan was such a happy child. It was also very painful and frightening to realize that our little boy was in such trouble. His teacher told us she could see the frustration on his face when he received his graded papers back in class.

The teacher conference deprived us of our denial. What she said was accurate and insightful. She gave us no false assurance and painted a picture of a potential grim reality which had to be faced. She did this in a nice way. I am sure she would have preferred to give us good news instead of the truth but the truth gave Jonathan what he needed. It gave him parents freed from their delusions and ready to face the fact that somehow Jonathan was lost and perhaps tragically so. Out of the desperation brought by the truth came the opportunity to show our unconditional love for Jonathan and our faithfulness, giving freely as only parents can give. Jonathan needed someone to believe in him, someone to fight for him. Although we had no idea what we were facing or what we would have to do, it was an honor to reach for our son.

And His disciples asked Him, saying, "Rabbi, who sinned, this man or his parents, that he should be born blind?" Jesus answered, "It was neither that this man sinned, nor his parents; but it was in order that the works of God might be displayed in him.

John 9:2,3.

Jesus therefore was saying to those Jews who had believed Him, "If you abide in My word, then you are truly disciples of Mine; and you

shall know the truth, and the truth shall make
you free." John 8:31, 32.

I began to work with Jonathan each evening
coming home earlier than usual so that I would
be able to spend the time necessary to help him
with his reading, spelling and math assignments.
This proved to be very time consuming but also
presented an opportunity to watch Jonathan
carefully as he turned to do his work.

Study for my first grader took the style of military boot camp. Still hopeful, I thought perhaps
he just did not want to work on his studies. So,
unorthodox as it may seem, I put my six year old
son "on the line," put on my drill instructor's hat
and began to teach Jonathan to spell at the top of

my lungs. His responses were just as loud and quite crisp. On the first night, the yelling went on for about three hours. Periodically, I would stop and ask him "Son, is this helping you?" His answer was always an enthusiastic "Yes!" It made me sad to realize that something was indeed wrong and that the little boy wanted so much to please his daddy. Later, his mother asked him if boot camp was helping. In a revealing answer, Jonathan said, "Yes. When Daddy's yelling at me, that's the only way I can hear it and I can't think of anything else." Jonathan's mother observed that my style of parenting was most unusual. But these were desperate times and Jonathan was learning his spelling lessons. Jonathan was learning, he was enjoying the attention of his father and if that's what it took to help Jonathan, I was more than willing. The yelling continued for days. I was concerned that with all the yelling the child might begin to think his role in life was to be yelled at. Of course, he was yelling at me as well. But I never missed an opportunity to compliment him, to hug him, to tell him how smart he was or tell him how much I loved him. He began to thirst for our study time together and I noticed that he was gaining confidence and that Jonathan was beginning to look at me when I spoke with him instead of the floor.

I also began to read with Jonathan. This was painful at first because Jonathan could barely read at all and every word was a struggle. Helping him get through three short paragraphs of "See Jane run." was an exhausting experience.

As he read, I studied Jonathan's every movement.

During one of the homework sessions I noticed something about Jonathan as he attempted to read. He was fidgeting with his toes, looking away from his book, scratching his arm and otherwise not paying much attention to the words on the page, even though I was standing over him like a drill instructor. He was also very frustrated and wanted to do anything but read. As I watched him struggle, it became clear to me that he was having difficulty focusing on the words. Nevertheless, boot camp seemed to be working. At the end of thirty days, Jonathan came to me wanting to read out loud. I knew he wanted to please his father and I was excited to find his reading had greatly improved. Over the course of the next couple of hours, Jonathan read out loud fifty-four pages of his first grade reader. This was a moment of great celebration for both of us and represented a real breakthrough. Although his grades were still all over the grading scale, Jonathan was much less frustrated and no longer cried out when it was time to go to school. He was, however, still different from my other children and had the tendency to be a loner and remained moody and distracted.

My wife was ahead of me in figuring out what we were looking at. She, of course, had struggled along with Jonathan living the same fear I was living only with the added depth of a mother's sensitivity. Fortunately, her curiosity and concern led her to several articles on ADD. She showed them to me. Jonathan fit most of the criteria and so did I.

Once my wife and I realized that our child was probably suffering from ADD we did what every concerned parent does—we began reading the vast material available on the Internet and in the bookstores. There were numerous expert explanations and gobs of psycho babble, most of which provided little hope without the use of drugs, but there was virtually no useful information for self management other than: get a routine, develop a reward system and hang on for the ride. Fortunately, I had met a family therapist in the course of my law practice for whom I had a developed a great deal of respect. I saw him in a bagel shop one Saturday morning and told him I needed to stop by. The decision to see a mental health professional was difficult for me to make. The thought of needing professional help in raising my son was something that my false sense of pride almost prevented. I also did not like the stigma which would come with formally diagnosing Jonathan with ADD. Love for Jonathan, however, and the desperation which engulfed me overcame my false pride and I set an appointment. Praise God. Meeting with the therapist proved to be a watershed event and set my compass in the search for Jonathan.

I met with Dr. Michael F. Zoda in October, 2000 explaining our situation, that I wanted to handle this issue parentally, that my wife and I were very much opposed to the use of drugs and that I wanted to meet with him rather than have Jonathan formally diagnosed. Dr. Zoda agreed with that approach because he believes parenting holds many of the keys to the development of coping tools needed to deal with the issues ADD brings. With this, Dr. Zoda began to explain some of the characteristics of ADD and what it was like to be ADD.

Dr. Zoda first explained that the affects of ADD ebb and flow to some degree. When the ADD child is "on" he relates to others better and seems to be more in tune with himself and the world. When he is "off" he is not able to relate to much of anything and seems to be at odds with everything and everybody. This sounds strange but the ADD parent will understand. Apparently the reason ADD children are given drugs is to allow them to focus and to be "on" more often. This information was consistent with our experience in that there were times Jonathan was easier to deal with and times when nothing seemed to fit together. But the thing I most remember about our initial conference is the description of how the ADD child experiences the world. Dr. Zoda painted a picture which is hard to forget and exposes the problem caused by ADD. He told me to envision looking at a display of sixteen different televisions sets each tuned to a different show and being equally interested in all sixteen programs. Remarkable. I thought of the impact. A little football, a little news, a little comedy, a little weather, a little sermon, a little business, a little PBS, a little movie, a little cooking, a little medical report, a little music, a little history, a little dog story, a little automobile, a little fishing, a little painting. There could be no consistent thought, no depth of information and certainly no learning or understanding. To further explain, he said that Jonathan would sit in class and be equally interested in the teacher, the bird outside, the child in the next row and the clock on the wall. It is exhausting to think about, but it explained a lot about Jonathan. It explained why he would become angry when he was trying to concentrate and someone would walk into the room. The distraction would pull him away from his work. It explained why he could not soak up enough information to do well on certain tests. He couldn't pay attention long enough to learn the material. It explained why he would leave out entire sections of school work. After starting a paper, his attention would be carried off and by the time he returned, he would have lost his place. It also explained why I could not stand the distraction of music playing while trying to work.

Dr. Zoda also cautioned me about my "boot camp" technique. He pointed out that one of the main goals of boot camp is to tear down the individual and to rebuild a man who understands the concept of working as a team. He wasn't necessarily against boot camp but felt that it should be used carefully. I have to confess I had not really looked at it from this angle and I did not like the thought of tearing Jonathan down. Boot camp had been very useful in that the structure exposed the distraction problem and appeared to have helped Jonathan to some degree. Regardless, although I kept some of the boot camp atmosphere, boot camp had served its purpose and was now over, except when Jonathan needed a sterner hand, which was not very often. Dr. Zoda also encouraged me to talk to Jonathan about what we were trying to do. His recommendation proved to be brilliant advice. Reflecting on this advice taught me a lot and changed the way I looked at the search for Jonathan.

I discovered that an ADD child is truly lost but he is lost inside himself. What I had to do was to search for Jonathan where he was which was behind that handsome face and beneath those light green eyes I loved so dearly. In order to reach my son, I needed more than the help Dr. Zoda could offer. I needed a partner. One who would always be there ready to help me and who was willing to take my hand and give me the support I needed. I found the help I needed from the little boy I was so desperately looking for and who was so willing to do anything I asked for so little as an approving glance.

My partner and I began to study his homework differently. Although I was still very much in control and the atmosphere was sometimes charged with military style command, we began to work together toward a common goal. Instead of drill sergeant and recruit, we became teacher and student and more importantly, father and son. There were still elements of boot camp discipline. I would not allow a tantrum or disinterest to interfere with our work. But before beginning each session, we would talk about what was helping and how Jonathan felt about what was going on.

The next several months brought great promise. I would work with Jonathan and he would work with me. We daily discussed how he was doing and worked on homework which slowly became much easier. At night we would thank God for his mercy and pray that God would mature Jonathan's mind. God does not disappoint. Because of what follows, we not only found

Jonathan but we also discovered he was a diamond in the rough.

One day shortly after I met with Dr. Zoda for the first time, I noticed that Jonathan could not hold his eyes on mine. His eyes would dart here and there. I barked out an order to look only in my eyes. No matter how loud I bellowed, he could not keep his eyes fixed on mine. Not only this, but when I told him he was looking away from my eyes, he denied it. He simply did not know he was taking his vision away from my eyes. It suddenly dawned on me that Jonathan not only had problems focusing, he did not know what it meant to focus. This made perfect sense. It would be impossible for someone who had spent his entire life out of focus and with his attention divided between sixteen different television sets, especially a six year old child, to understand what it meant to focus. How could I expect him to focus if he did not know what it meant to focus? I knew immediately that this was the first clue on how to reach Jonathan. So I stopped and told Jonathan that he needed to learn how to focus and that being able to focus meant being able to think about only one thing.

The next day, before Jonathan and I began to study, I told him again that being able to focus meant being able to think about only one thing. We then began look into each other's eyes. As usual, I would not allow him to move and he had to stand at attention. His eyes were darting around looking at one thing and then another.

Whenever I spoke to him about looking away, he would deny it again and again. Suddenly, I caught him looking at something behind me and outside. I said loudly, "You're looking at something outside! What is it?!" Surprised by the sudden sharpness of my question, he realized he was not looking in my eyes and told me he was looking at a bug on the patio. I told him that if he was looking at the bug outside, he was not focusing on my eyes because being able to focus meant being able to think about only one thing. I could see by the look on his face that for the first time he understood the idea of focusing. Shortly after this, Jonathan began to look directly into my eyes with a penetrating, laser like gaze. I would have him practice this by "locking down" on unsuspecting friends who happened by.

Jonathan's stare was so piercing it took on a haunting quality. This was greatly encouraged and celebrated.

Jonathan responded very positively to looking directly into my eyes. Sometimes this took the character of a stare down game. My other sons also found this to be exciting and for weeks the boys would have staring contests. On almost every occasion, Jonathan would win. This in and of itself was a huge improvement and a confidence builder for Jonathan. Dr. Zoda had told me that Jonathan's inability to look at me in my eyes was probably an indication of low self esteem. For whatever it meant, Jonathan no longer had that particular problem and by all indications was feeling better about himself. His grades, however, showed no improvement and I continued to see Dr. Zoda.

Teaching Jonathan to spell was always very hard. I would call out a word but he could not spell it. I would spell it and ask him to repeat it. He could not. Again, I would spell the word and ask him to repeat it, and he could not. This would go on for hours. Then we came upon the word "cat." I was pretty frustrated and felt like every kid should know how to spell "cat." When he couldn't spell it even after ten attempts, I realized that Jonathan simply did not have the ability to remember things. He had almost no short term memory. Suddenly I started throwing out a series of four single digit numbers and telling him to repeat them. He couldn't do it, so I tried three numbers. It took about fifteen tries for him to successfully repeat a series of three. I tried it again and again. Although Jonathan had little success at repeating the numbers, the events that evening triggered my imagination. I thought about what this might mean. I reasoned that if Jonathan had no short term memory, he could not take in the information necessary to learn his lessons. Even if he were the brightest child in school but had no memory, he would not be successful in class.

I was then graced with an idea. Perhaps Jonathan could work his way into focus by performing a series of increasingly difficult mental tasks. The tasks would be designed to require progressively greater concentration. The first tasks would be our conversation and staring into each other's eyes. The second tasks would be the oral recall of a series of numbers, first two series of three numbers, then two series of four numbers. The third tasks would be the recall of two series of three written numbers and then two series of four written numbers. So before school one morning in January, Jonathan and I went to the dining room table and I gave him what was to be the first mental exercise which, with modification, would be repeated every morning since that time. We didn't know it but we were about to find our needle in the haystack.

There was something different about Jonathan when I gave him the exercise. He seemed crisp, a little more in control. His behavior was improved and he played better. He even seemed to hit the baseball better. I then analyzed the exercise more deeply to see what we had done.

It seemed that in repeating numbers, there were two variables—order and number. This means that Jonathan had to remember eight bits of information in repeating a set of four written or oral numbers. If I added color to the written exercise, that would make the exercise harder and would require Jonathan to remember twelve bits of information for a series of four written numbers—number, order and color. I also reasoned that numbers are easy to use and even a series of numbers makes sense. If I used symbols—a blue square, red triangle, orange circle, green cross—this would make the exercise even more challenging because the symbols would have no meaning when strung together. Jonathan took to the exercise immediately.

I then noticed that Jonathan's ability to do the morning exercise was growing stronger and that when he did the exercise he was "on" all day. So I changed the exercise increasing the number of colored symbols to a series of five and then six. To make it even more challenging, I began mixing in letters and numbers with the symbols, each with a different color. Four weeks after beginning the exercise Jonathan was able to complete the exercise ending with a series of seven symbols, numbers and letters, all of a different color. The form of the exercise was now complete.

The morning exercise had quite an impact on our family. There were no morning conflicts, no discipline problems to deal with and no crying in the morning. The effects of the exercise were also being seen by Jonathan's teacher. Although his grades had not greatly improved, the teacher said she had noticed that Jonathan was more focused and that he was now participating much better in class. She reported that he would now laugh at times when it was appropriate. Although it was clear that Jonathan was not where she wanted him to be she liked the trend and hoped it would continue. I reported all this to Dr. Zoda and brought him a partial example of the exercise. He wanted to know how long it took. I told him about twenty-five minutes. He also wanted to know if I had to give the exercise more than once a day. I told him we did not and that after giving the exercise, Jonathan appeared to be "on" all day long. Dr. Zoda encouraged me to continue the exercise and suggested an incentive point system to encourage Jonathan's participation. So I told Jonathan he had earned about ten toy points. I also told him that for each day he completed the exercise successfully, he would get another point and when he wanted to, he could trade the points in for toys. This proved to be a great for Jonathan's motivation.

I also told Dr. Zoda about something strange which had happened a few weeks before. On the weekend of March 8th, I decided I had been working Jonathan pretty hard and that maybe he should be given a break from doing the exercise.

He had been doing it every day for almost two months. This proved to be a mistake. On Saturday morning, we gave a birthday party for our other two sons. Jonathan did not do very well at the party and his mother noticed that he was complaining and getting into trouble. Jonathan also told me that he didn't have any fun at the party. The next morning as we were getting ready to go to church, Jonathan pitched a tantrum like we had not seen in months. He was crying and screaming and was extremely frustrated. He had been in trouble with his brothers and his mother and just would not stop. He did not respond to discipline. I told my wife that I had to give him the exercise. The exercise took an entire hour to complete. But after it was over, he suddenly stopped crying and was calm. I asked him how he felt. His exact words were "I feel a lot better." Dr. Zoda told me to keep talking to Jonathan about the exercise and how he felt about it and by all means to continue to give it to Jonathan.

By the end of the school year, Jonathan had become even stronger at performing the exercise. He now was repeating two sets of four oral numbers, then two sets of five oral numbers. I would then give him two sets of five written numbers and two sets of six written numbers. Finally, I would give him eleven different symbols all of a different color for recall. To do so, Jonathan had to recall thirty-three bits of information—eleven colors, eleven symbols and eleven positions. For example, I would use a blue cross, red 4, purple Y, green box, orange Q, pink X, yellow 9, black T, pencil moon, blue pen W, gray star. He almost always got this correct. Even if he didn't I was still quite pleased. After all, the idea was to get him into focus, which the exercise was doing quite well. I did find it necessary to have him successfully complete the eye contact, the oral numbers and the written numbers correctly.

By now, I was asking Jonathan how he was feeling when he came in each morning and how he felt after the exercise. He told me he always felt much better after the exercise. So one morning I asked him to explain to me how he thought the exercise helped him. He said, "It's like my mind is a puzzle and this puts it together. It helps me think better." Sometime over the next several days, he told me that the exercise was "like a key to my mind." When I reported this to Dr. Zoda he told me that those are the same types of comments that children make after taking prescription drugs to help them focus. I also asked Jonathan if he knew why the exercise was making him feel better. He said he sometimes felt better when repeating the oral numbers. He usually felt better after repeating the written numbers. But after he repeated the colored symbols he always felt much, much better.

The ADD child is famous for being impatient. This impatience invades everything he does. So when I saw Jonathan read, I realized he was still lost in ADD. Although by now, Jonathan was reading books beyond his grade level, when he read out loud, he would leave off the endings of some words and would skip words in almost every paragraph. Although I would correct him each time, he would do the same thing on each paragraph. I spoke to a reading specialist who told me this was normal for a seven year old child. But I saw something different in what Jonathan was doing. He was unable to read all the words with all the proper endings. This was due to the impatience of ADD. So I thought of myself and of my impatience and of the many times when I could not read all the words and all the endings on all the pages. What I knew is what the impatience did to Jonathan as he tried to read. It made it all but impossible to keep his eyes from flying past words on the page, sometimes going line by line from left to right without stopping long enough to see the words. This explained why he left off endings to words and why he would constantly leave out words and why he did not do well on reading tests. So I told him to do what I do. I told him to look at each and every word before moving on. I had seen my father do this. I do it and my son will do this as well. As Dr. Zoda had encouraged, I then explained to him that words are information and without picking up all the information, he could not answer questions about what he had read. I showed him some reading exercises my wife had found and taught him to read the instructions word for word, three times. I told him to look at the page of the reading exercise and all around it to see where the all test questions were located.

His reading flourished and he began to score highly on the reading exercises. We continued all through the summer to do the morning exercises which by now had progressed to thirteen colored symbols.

Victory came in the fall. It was full and complete. At the beginning of the second week of second grade, I met with Jonathan's teacher. Still fearful, I explained that I was concerned because of Jonathan's focusing problem. She looked surprised and said she had seen nothing like that. I asked about how he was doing in his work. She told me it was excellent. She also said Jonathan was a model student and that she was using him as the class example of how to behave. The first week's papers came home. He had no grade

lower than an A. Everyday I would tell Jonathan
to read the instructions word for word three
times, to look at the work sheet to see where all
the questions were and to check his work answer
by answer. At the end of the first nine weeks we
went to the school's open house to receive
Jonathan's report card. When Jonathan's enve-
lope was handed to my wife, a blue ribbon fell
out revealing he had made the all A honor roll.

In his infinite wisdom God gives each of us certain gifts. Sometimes the gifts are apparent,
sometimes they are not. I was given the gift of
being ADD so that when I heard a small voice
crying out, I would know how to find Jonathan.
Whatever disappointments I may have experienced as a child now merely enhance the joy of

seeing Jonathan rise. I know my child as he is now and I know the pain he will never experience.

There is something strange about ADD. It happens every day. When my baby goes to sleep each evening, ADD comes in like a thief and takes him away again. I only know one way in to get him out of the hell of ADD, and I have to go in to get him every morning. Sometimes it's hard to find him. But I get him every time. Sometimes he fights with me. But I get him every time. Sometimes it's a painful trip in. But I get him every time. Now that I know how to save him, I have to do it every day. And I can tell you that every day, Daddy's coming in.

... Quickly bring out the best robe and put it on him, and put a ring on his hand and sandals on his feet; and bring the fattened calf, kill it, and let us eat and be merry; for this son of mine was dead, and has come to life again; he was lost, and has been found. Luke 15:22-24.

And not only this, but we exult in our tribulations knowing that tribulation brings about perseverance; and perseverance, proven character; proven character, hope; and hope does not disappoint, because the love of God has been poured out within our hearts through the Holy Spirit who was given to us. Rom. 5:3-5.

Epilogue

The morning exercise has dramatically improved my son's life and the well being of our family. Whereas before the exercise, my wife and I had two well adjusted children and one in a desperate struggle, we now have three successful children and peace in the home. As every family member knows, peace in the home is not possible when one of the members is deeply troubled.

I have to stress that Jonathan has not been formally diagnosed with Attention Deficit Disorder. As everyone knows, a diagnosis of ADD brings with it a lot of baggage both from our schools and from society in general. We simply did not want to burden our son with the ADD label. However, the fact that Jonathan has ADD has been informally confirmed by a mental health care professional and can be seen by the observations made in this book. Moreover, two other children who have been formally diagnosed with ADD have used these techniques with results similar to and just as wonderful as those seen in Jonathan. I am not claiming that this exercise is appropriate for other children. That would be a question for a mental health care professional. What I do know is that the current regimen of drug therapy is unacceptable for my son. I also know that Jonathan through the exercise is essentially asymptomatic. No longer does my little boy cry and scream before rising each morning. No longer does my son curl up in his blanket under the kitchen table pleading for help at dawn. Instead, he comes to my bedside, happy, face washed, and fully dressed saying, " It's time for my numbers, Daddy."

The following is an abbreviated documentation of the results and my personal observations as well as an outline of the exercise protocol.

RESULTS

The child experienced some improvement within two weeks of beginning the exercise. The initial improvement centered on a lower level of frustration and improved ability to spell. As the exercise was consistently performed, the improvement became more apparent. The following results occurred within four months. The child became very peaceful and less stressed. The child virtually never cried in the morning, and the before school routine became very pleasant and more compliant. The scholastic performance improved, and the teacher reported strongly improved classroom participation, greater confidence and reduced frustration. The child's self perception became excellent. The child's teacher was very pleased with the results, although initially the child's grades did not dramatically improve. As noted, after successfully completing the exercise, the child's ability to focus began to be maintained all day long. Although the child often had some difficulty in performing the tasks in the morning, over time, the child's ability to perform the exercise greatly improved and the morning routine became easier for him. Additionally, the incidents of the child being out of focus dramatically decreased.

After working with the child for approximately eight months, a new school year began (second grade) with astonishing results. The child was selected as <u>student of the day</u> twice in the first seven days and in music class on the first meeting. The child's first week's schoolwork papers were equally outstanding. Out of 261 required responses, the child had given 260 correct answers. The new teacher who was unaware of the child's previous behavior told me that she periodically uses the child as a model for how the class should behave. She also reported to me that the child's oral reading is the best at his table. The child is delighted with school. The child achieved an all A report card for the first nine weeks of second grade. The family is less stressed and filled with hope and a sense of profound gratitude. It should be noted that the child still exhibits some of the ADD traits such as standing up at the table and being talkative.

These behavior patterns are now so modified that they are not at all a disruption but merely a representation of the child's personality. I believe the exercise has allowed the child to self govern his behavior so that the child inside has an opportunity to develop and reveal himself. It is noteworthy that the child always reports he feels better after the exercise is completed, regardless of whether he is completely successful in performing the exercise. The therapist with whom I have consulted notes that the child speaks about feeling better after completing the exercise in the same way that children who take the typically prescribed drugs speak about feeling better after taking their medicine.

VIII. COMMENTS

The child has applied the focusing skills learned during the described process to the classroom. I told the child to look at the teacher in the eyes when she is talking and not to look at anything else. The teacher reports that the child is doing just as directed. I have also told him to read the instructions word for word, three times, and not to skip over any words. I also told him to look at the whole page before beginning an assignment and to check over his work after completion. These instructions would have been meaningless prior to the exercise.

It should be noted that this process is difficult for both the child and the adult. The adult must be prepared to stick with the program and to love the child enough to push the child out of the child's comfort zone. It also is very helpful to explain to the child what the goals are and why the child is going through this process. I would stress that I have found it very important to allow the child the feeling of success and encouragement. As mentioned, a reward system is very helpful and can also be used to teach the child other beneficial lessons such as saving money, the value of money and work ethic.

Since the adult is the arbiter of what is a successful exercise for the child, the adult can assure the child is successful by making the goals obtainable and yet challenging. Making the exercise a challenge brings results although sometimes with resistance, and even a few rare tears.

This method and exercise has been a direct answer to prayer. Now, our family's deepest fears are eased and we have been left with a profound sense of gratitude. It is difficult to describe our joy seeing our child overcome what had previously seemed an imposing obstacle. Without the extraordinary guidance of Christ, the very dramatic success of my son would not have been possible. I would also like to point out that Dr. Mike Zoda, a family therapist in Tallahassee, Florida, has given extremely valuable advice with respect to this issue. **It is the author's view that the exercises and process described herein should only be attempted**

with the continuing guidance and advice of a
trained mental health care professional.

PARENTAL MANAGEMENT TECHNIQUES FOR THE ATTENTION DEFICIT DISORDER CHILD

SUMMARY:

The essential idea is that the child can work his way into focus by performing tasks of increasing complexity. A summary of the steps of the exercise would be as follows:

1. Staring in parent's eyes
2. Four oral numbers for recall (twice)
3. Five oral numbers for recall (twice)
4. Five written numbers for recall (twice)
5. Six written numbers for recall

(twice)

6. Four to six multicolored written symbols for recall

7. If child is unable to do tasks 1 through 5, try fewer numbers/symbols for each tasks.

8. Increase number of multicolored written symbols as the child's ability improves up to approximately fourteen to sixteen

I. Perceived Problem

Child meets many of the criteria consistent with a diagnosis of Attention Deficit/ Hyperactivity Disorder. Child is highly frustrated and unable to focus and therefore has difficulty in reading, paying attention in class and difficulty in following instructions. Stress in the family is very high centering on the ADD child's behavior. The family does not want to resort to traditional methods of managing the child and is particularly opposed to drug therapy.

II. Observations

1. Child is often extremely frustrated in the morning (2-3 mornings each week). This is observably demonstrated by screaming and kicking before he leaves the bed. The child frequently curls up in the fetal position in a blanket near the breakfast table and cries after leav-

ing the bed. The child is difficult to get dressed, fights putting on socks and shoes by repeatedly refitting socks and shoes on feet. Cries often in the morning.

2. The child is often disobedient and obstinate, requiring discipline before school. This is very disruptive for the entire family.

3. When he returns home from school, the child cries if parent does not go directly home.

4. Will not look parent in the eyes.

5. The child has difficulty in making up his mind on what to do or what to buy such as choosing toys or treats at the bakery counter. Even

after making a choice, the child suffers buyer's remorse.

6. Changes personality at school in that at home he is happy go lucky (not including mornings before school) but, at school, the teacher reports that he does not laugh even when it would be appropriate to do so and rarely smiles at school.

7. Child is described by the teacher as calm, quiet, not a discipline problem, but not engaged.

8. Teacher reports child has difficulty in maintaining attention.

9. Grades range from A to F with many on the lower end.

10. Teacher tells parents that she

believes the child may well have a processing problem.

11. Child has inability to spell three and four letter words even after reviewing.

12. School work reflects that the child leaves out entire sections of work on daily work assignment and test.

13. Child is unable to read three short paragraphs without much frustration and resistance.

14. The child will not do schoolwork with mother and fights her doing homework.

15. Any distraction in the room or classroom where child is attempting to work (sometimes even if

noise is at other end of house) will cause an angry outburst by the child.

16. When taking a nap or going to sleep at night, child fights going to sleep and squirms, crying out in apparent frustration.

17. Social interaction is not always a positive experience. The child often irritates siblings by poking, jabbing, etc.

18. Child has problem sitting at table or staying still.

III. Stated Goal:

1. Manage the child's ADD condi-

tion by:

a. teaching him what it means to focus.

b. teaching him how to narrow his field of focus by giving a series of multifaceted tasks of increasing complexity to perform each morning.

c. Once the child understands what it means to focus and how to narrow the field of focus, teaching him methods of learning which support his new ability to concentrate.

IV. Assumptions

1. Child suffers from Attention Deficit Disorder.

2. Child has the ability to perform a series of multifaceted tasks.

3. Child does not understand what it means to focus or narrow point of concentration.

4. A child can be taught to focus on a narrow field.

5. Memorizing a series of numbers, letters or symbols of various colors cannot be accomplished without developing the skill of focusing on a narrow field.

6. The ability to narrow the field of

focus will allow the child to absorb more information, improve his scholastic performance, reduce child's stress and mental fatigue.

7. Remembering oral commands and remembering written commands requires different skills.

8. Appropriate judgment can not be developed unless the child can absorb complete information about a subject matter and has practice in working with a complete set of facts as applied to life situations.

9. The inability to form appropriate judgments about a subject matter would results in lower self-confidence and poor self esteem.

V. Methodology

1. The child should be accurately evaluated for the capacity to perform the exercise. This should be done in consultation with a mental health care professional. It is critical that the exercise be performed only by a child capable of succeeding in doing the exercise.

2. Explain to child that focusing means being able to think about only one thing.

3. Child should be placed in "boot camp" atmosphere to provide structure and to orient the child to taking specific directions without margin

for error.

4. During boot camp, parent does not allow the child to move feet, hands or eyes when listening to or responding to instructions.

5. Child is required to look directly in the eyes of the parent during instructions. If the child looks away from parents eyes during instructions, immediately, abruptly and loudly stop the child with "YOU LOOKED AWAY FROM ME! YOU WERE FOCUSING ON SOMETHING OTHER THAN WHAT I AM TALKING ABOUT!" Immediately identify what the child looked at other than the parents eyes

and discuss with the child. This will hopefully demonstrate to the child that looking elsewhere is an indication of distraction from assigned task and a lack of focus. Make the child look directly into the parent's eyes for further instructions and reinforce point two above (explain that focusing means being able to think about only one thing). Making the child understand the concept of <u>focusing</u> is extraordinarily important. For example, as the child's interest is drawn away by a passing butterfly, bring his attention back and explain that he broke his focus. The child must understand the concept of focusing to be able to avoid temptation of distraction.

6. Parent gives a series of simple tasks for the child to do (such as go to the door, knock three times, return to me, tell me you did it, go to the kitchen, return to me, stand in front of me and tell me "I'm finished."). Repeat a number of times with different tasks.

7. Child should not be allowed to use a tantrum to attempt avoid doing task. Remember that following instructions is difficult for the child and apply love and praise liberally when instructions are followed. Yet at the same time do not allow room for the

child to err (this means that the parent must accurately evaluate the capacity of the child to follow instructions and to complete tasks). The parent should adjust the difficulty of the task for the particular child to assure that the child can successfully complete task. Part of the intent is to encourage the child and build momentum based on much positive reinforcement with a foundation built on success. Explain to the child that parent loves the child regardless of how well the child performs the tasks to assure the child that his or her value is not based on performance of tasks. A

reward system works well particularly when rewards are immediate.

8. Having made point 7, strict discipline of both parent and child is
required in order for the child to
realize that although following
instructions is difficult for the child,
the child must complete the tasks or
will be required to do it over.   Child
need not perform tasks in point 1
through 8 after mastering the concept of focusing on specific tasks.
Once this has been achieved, child
should begin each morning with
THE EXECISE.

9. Complete **THE EXERCISE** <u>**each**</u>
<u>**morning.**</u>

VI. THE EXERCISE

1. Child is required to look directly into the eyes of the parent for approximately 30 seconds. If the child does not continually look directly and **exclusively** into the parent's eyes, stop to explain to the child that he or she is distracted and not focused. Try to identify what the child is looking at and explain that the child can not look at the object and focus on the parent's eyes at the same time. It is not unusual for the child to look elsewhere without realizing he or she has broken focus. Repeat this portion of the exercise

and require the child to look directly in the parent's eyes for 30 seconds.

2. Orally give child a series of 4 randomly selected numbers (parent may need to use 3 numbers initially depending on the child's ability) and ask for immediate recall (such as 10, 5, 14, 9). Remember that the child must look parent in the eyes and no where else. Parent should realize there are eight tasks involved—recalling 4 numbers, in the correct order. For variety, 4 letters might be used (such as D, N, Q, G) or even colors or objects for a younger child (e.g. dog, tree, cloud, book).

3. When child has successfully completed the oral task 2 times, give the child 5 oral numbers for oral recall. Repeat a second time. Again, if the child is unable recall the numbers successfully, begin with 3 numbers and during the same session, move to 4 numbers.

4. When the child has successfully completed two sets of 4 oral numbers for recall and two sets of 5 oral numbers for recall, write a series 5 written numbers on a piece of paper. Let the child study the numbers as long as he likes. Ask the child to turn over the paper and write the numbers by memory. Repeat. When the child has

successfully recalled 2 series of 5 written numbers or letters, repeat twice using 6 written numbers or letters. Again, if the child is unable to perform this written tasks, begin with 3 written numbers and move to 4 written numbers in the same session.

5. If child is able to successfully complete written recall tasks, write 4 symbols, letters and numbers in different colors. Vary the order and color of the symbols. The parent should realize this requires remembering 12 bits of information—4 colors, 4 symbols in correct order. An example would be:

orange G, blue circle, red 4, green cross

6. Increase the number of different colored symbols as ability of the child improves.

Over time, hopefully, the child will be able to remember more colored symbols of greater variety. The author's experience was that the child's ability to perform these tasks increased rapidly, greatly improving his ability to recall. In a four week period of time, the child on whom this exercise was tried improved from successfully completing a four symbol task to successfully completing a task consisting of a series of 7 letters, symbols and numbers such as:

red X, green 23, blue square, orange triangle, purple 98, yellow 39, black A

After approximately seven months of performing this exercise every morning, the child improved so that he was able to consistently recall a series of 13 different numbers, letters and symbols. This requires remembering 39 bits of information— 13 symbols, 13 colors in correct order. NOTE: When the child is easily able to perform the task, the number of symbols should increase. There is a limit to the number of symbols the parent will want to use. The parent should remember that the purpose of the exercise is to teach the child how to focus and to get the child focused. Successfully completing the task is a secondary concern.

7. The Exercise **must** be completed **every day**. The author notes that the

child starts off each day with the inability to focus. However, once the child is focused, the child remains focused all day. There is one partial exception. Initially, if the child took a nap, he would need to be refocused. Over time, however, the child began to remain focused even after he took a nap. Sometimes the problem is more apparent than at other times. Nevertheless, the parent should consider that the child needs the exercise each morning and that the purpose of the exercise is to take the child from a state of not being able to focus to a state of being able to focus. Restated differently, the exercise should be viewed as method of bringing the child from a state of disbursed attention to a state of focused attention. If the exercise is not completed every day, the child becomes very frustrated and irritable. It is helpful to do the exercise in the morning to help organize the child's thoughts for the day. It may also be helpful to initially give the child a series of oral numbers at various times during the day.

8. The child on whom the exercise has been tried may well go through various stages of resistance as he is per-

forming the exercise and forcing his scope of concentration to a narrow field, in this case, the symbols, letters and numbers. The child will often experience an irresistible tickle, itch, cough or other distraction. This will sometimes result in a burst of frustration. The parent will need to develop the skill of helping the child work through this frustration. The author believes that all children experience distractions such as an itch, a tickle in the throat or a minor pain in the leg. The ADD child, however, has a heightened awareness of many normal distractions but has limited ability to ignore or disregard the distraction. The author believes this is simply a magnification of senses that the child becomes aware of as consequence of attempting to do something difficult, in this case performing the focusing exercise. This behavior is similar to the crying and kicking which formerly was seen in the morning prior to the child leaving his bed or immediately prior to a nap or going to sleep.

Examples of the Exercise

The following are examples of the exercise at three different levels through which Jonathan progressed. Each exercise session began with me and Jonathan staring into each other's eyes for approximately thirty seconds. Over time, I made the exercise progressively more difficult but always kept in mind the idea that Jonathan could work his way into focus by performing a series of tasks of increasing complexity. In the last step of each exercise, Jonathan is required to study and then recall a series of symbols consisting of letters, numbers, and symbols (e.g. a square or star) each of a different color. Beneath each symbol, I have provided an example of a color which might be used. The oral and written numbers for recall change every time the exercise is given. Similarly, the color, symbol, and position of the colored symbols change with every exercise. I allow Jonathan to study the exercise as long as he needs to, but encourage him to do it as quickly as possible.

As Jonathan would advance, I would add one colored symbol to the last step of each exercise. He stayed at that level until he could write all the colored symbols on recall consistently. By consistently, I mean four to five times each week.

At that point, I would add another colored symbol. He is currently at fourteen colored symbols for written recall. He began doing the exercise with three colored symbols.

I have found it very important to complete all three segments of the exercise, <u>every day</u>. This exercise represents an intentional focusing of the child. It must be done in a loving manner with a lot of encouragement during and after the exercise and, in my view, with the advice of a qualified mental health care provider.

Example of the Exercise (Initial Stage)

For oral recall:
(four sets)
Parent gives first set of numbers to the child orally and requires the child

First set:	12	7
Second set:	9	16
Third set:	7	5
Fourth set:	18	2

At this level, the child has to remember six or eight bits of information

---

For written recall:
(four sets)
Parent writes down the first set of numbers requiring the child to study
Repeat with second, third and fourth sets.

First set:	21	8
Second set:	42	9
Third set:	5	17
Fourth set:	9	16

At this level, the child has to remember eight or ten bits of information

---

For written recall:
(colored symbols)
(one set)
Parent writes down the set of symbols in color and requires the child to
the correct position and in the correct color.

☐	A
(blue)	(red)

At this level, the child has to remember fifteen bits of information {three
color-orange} in order to write on recall the colored symbols.

orally recall first set. Repeat with second, third and fourth sets.

```
 8
40
24      6
15      1
```

r each set (correct number in correct order).

_____

e set. The child is then required to write the set of numbers from memory.

```
15      7
12     63
 3     20     14
45     12      7
```

r each set (correct number in correct order).

_____

dy the set of symbols and to write down from memory the symbols in

```
 7           O          *
range)     (green)    (black)
```

ts of information for each position: (1) symbol-7 (2) position-3rd (3)

Example of the Exercise (Intermediate Stage)

For oral recall:
(four sets)

Parent gives first set of numbers to the child orally and requires the child

First set:	17	5
Second set:	13	1
Third set:	52	6
Fourth set:	18	9

At this level, the child has to remember eight or ten bits of information

---

For written recall:
(four sets)

Parent writes down the first set of numbers requiring the child to study
Repeat with second, third and fourth sets.

First set:	24	13
Second set:	39	7
Third set:	12	41
Fourth set:	79	36

At this level, the child has to remember ten or twelve bits of information

---

For written recall:
(colored symbols)
(one set)

Parent writes down the set of symbols in color and requires the child to
the correct position and in the correct color.

*	Y	△	4
(red)	(blue)	(green)	(red)

At this level, the child has to remember twenty-four bits of information
(3) color-blue} in order to write on recall the colored symbols.

to orally recall first set. Repeat with second, third and fourth sets.

22	9	
84	3	
19	4	7
67	3	8

for each set (correct number in correct order).

___

the set. The child is then required to write the set of numbers from memory.

95	88	6	
52	19	28	
75	89	33	64
81	52	48	27

for each set (correct number in correct order).

___

study the set of symbols and to write down from memory the symbols in

U	9	Z	☐
(yellow)	(purple)	(orange)	(brown)

{three bits of information for each position: (1) symbol-Y (2) position-2nd

Example of the Exercise (Advanced Stage)

For oral recall:

(four sets)

Parent gives first set of numbers to the child orally and requires the child

First set:	18	45
Second set:	39	82
Third set:	28	31
Fourth set:	72	49

At this level, the child has to remember eight or ten bits of information

---

For written recall:

(four sets)

Parent writes down the first set of numbers requiring the child to study
Repeat with second, third and fourth sets.

First set:	69	75
Second set:	94	37
Third set:	25	18
Fourth set:	17	59

At this level, the child has to remember ten or twelve bits of information

---

For written recall:

(colored symbols)

(one set)

Parent writes down the set of symbols in color and requires the child to
the correct position and in the correct color.

△	Y	Z	✔	7	*	U
(yellow)	(green)	(red)	(black)	(purple)	(orange)	(brown)

At this level, the child has to remember forty-two of information {three
color-brown} in order to write on recall the colored symbols.

to orally recall first set. Repeat with second, third and fourth sets.

29	37	
56	97	
55	64	79
53	28	15

for each set (correct number in correct order).

---

the set. The child is then required to write the set of numbers from memory.

41	13	22	
28	61	53	
73	47	61	32
68	24	36	49

for each set (correct number in correct order).

---

study the set of symbols and to write down from memory the symbols in

5	Q	▢	9	K	4	+
(pencil)	(red pen)	(gray crayon)	(pink)	(blue)	(light green)	(black pen)

bits of information for each position: (1) symbol-U (2) position-7th (3)

Printed in the United States
928700004B